The Red All Over Riddle Book

The Red All Over Riddle Book

George Szirtes

illustrated by Andrew Stooke

faber and faber
LONDON · BOSTON

First published in 1997
by Faber and Faber Limited
3 Queen Square London WC1N 3AU

Typeset by Faber and Faber Ltd
Printed and bound in Great Britain by
Clays Ltd, St Ives plc

A CIP record for this book
is available from the British Library

ISBN 0–571–17807–3

10 9 8 7 6 5 4 3 2 1

for John Mole and John Cotton
who riddled before
and Jane Feaver
who suggested I should

1 We push his nose when we want in
   And he must squeal or chime or sing,
   Like dentists we say, *Open wide!*
   And once that's done we slip inside.

2 On the top sits fire,
   In the middle gold
   At the bottom grass.

   At the top you stop
   In the middle wait
   And at the bottom, pass.

3 Fire in water
   A delicate flick of flame

   All glow, gape and gill,
   Now darting, now still

   The soul
   Of the bowl

   But leisurely, leisurely,
   Sunken treasurely.

4   A tiny roar
    at the tip of a stick,
    one live shimmering feather,

    then a luminous bird flapping scarlet wings
    to the hot beat of its heart,

    with feathers everywhere
    crackling and cooing
    fluttering, devouring,

    the blackened bough it sits on.

5 Here come the angels
   Like very loud tourists
   Wielding their cameras
   With built in flashes
   Brightening dark weather.

6 Where am I? I do not know, I sit
   Inside that girl. It's very dark. Between
   My looking and her thinking is a space
   For one whom neither she nor I have seen,
   Who looks and thinks and in the darkness stirs
   And dreams of us, or thinks the dream is hers.

7 Whoever invented it
   must be turning in his grave

   Whoever fitted it
   must be rolling in it

   Whoever thought of a square one
   must be a strange felloe.

8 They tend to go round in circles
While coming straight to the point,
Have barely a leg to stand on
With only a single hip-joint

They pirouette, they twist around
With one black stump, one foot unshod
And leave small holes where they have trod.

9 His flat face may look like a light switch
   and
   his eyes like a pair of saucers
   and
   his beak like tiny tin-snips
   and
   his body like a soft pellet
   but
   to who?

10   Firm in the saddle,
     Riding the full force
     Of the world as it strikes you,
     They clear a way for you.

     Later, in bed
     They lie quietly,
     Folding their arms and examining
     Their own delicate wrists.

11 Two wheels rolled along
A man sat in the middle
Although he had no horse
He sat firm in the saddle
Although he had no car
He still pressed on the pedal
And so his feet went round
Both feet off the ground.

12 Time has handcuffed us:
    Its small round face insists
    We measure our own pulse
    By glancing at our wrists.

13 All that breathing, heaving, running, steaming
    All that mane and hoof and eye,
    As if a simple block of wood were dreaming
    And, in a vision, seemed to gallop by
    While merely toing-and-froing,
    Both standing still and going.

14 Squeaking not crowing
Never quite going
But pretty well knowing
Which way the wind's blowing.

clothes Peg

15　I cling on in desperation
　　Grip the line and bob and pray
　　When wild storms rage through the garden
　　They won't blow your clothes away.
　　And now they're dry, do you intend
　　to keep me hanging on all day?

16 All too liable to snap
    And light as a feather,
    But willing to stretch the odd point
    So when everything is threatening
    To fall apart
    It holds together.

17 They cover your ear
    They cover your lip
    They cram you with words
    they give you the pip.

*

One chirrups on the table
Until you pick her up
And comfort her, poor thing,
But then you have to listen
To her endless nattering.

18   What makes him glow like that
      Through his blood-red waistcoat
      As if he had swallowed the sun
      Or one small portion of it
      To keep him going
      All through winter?

19 I saw a bride splendid in white garments.
    I saw a woman with one hundred children
    The children plump and firm within her arms.
    But some fell down or strangers took and ate them,
    Cut them, sliced them, bit them, baked them,
       boiled them –
    Alas, alas, a widow frail and naked
    stood by my window in the heavy snow
    Imagining, under the white snow, she was a bride
    again.
    In time, she sighed, in time.

F   L

A   G

20 To some a source of pride
     To some a sheet of grief,
     A kind of gaudy tie
     Or giant handkerchief.

21 Light fingered, invisible
    A thief through and through
    He'll steal your hat, he'll whip your scarf
    And your newspaper too.
    He'll hang around street corners
    And pounce as you go by
    Or hover at your window
    And slip in with a sigh.

22   Shimmering shimmering
   Like stroking a cat the wrong way
   The green turning silver
   And the whole field
   Shimmering shimmering.

23 So much water
The earth drinks down
You'd think poor little squiggly worms
Might well drown

And all the ants and beetles
And other creepy things
Rush round in a panic
Wearing water wings.

24 Above the green carpet
The great fried egg
Sits in his blue bath.

25　Ten moons, twenty moons,
    Adult moons, baby moons,
    Sharp little moons
    Bent on fingers of cloud
    Growing night and day

    Then shorn away.

26 The first was the broadest
The second pointed the way
The third, the tallest, followed
The fourth one had the ring
The last, stuck on the end, was weakest.
Each found a key
all of them danced to music.
Who were they?

27 A tongue that never speaks,
   A skin that's black or brown
   going out for walks
   But never on his own.

28 Tiny black beetles march in a line
    But when you turn a new leaf over
    Their spirits take wing
    In your head.

29 Time is frozen in a box –
   A flat tide in the dark –
   The world resurfaces, a distant echo,
   A stiff paper, bearing all our faces.

30 Look at him nibbling the page
Leaving the blue behind,
How efficient he must be,
So thin and straight and tall,
And always on the ball.

31 Here they come
     Dancing on points
     Doing the splits
     Cold hearted dancers
     With sharp cutting answers.

32 The more you hold him
The thinner he grows,
The wetter he gets
The brighter he glows,

The lither and leaner
The slimmer his shape,
The more likely he is
To want to escape.

The more he escapes
The more he grows leaner
Each time you touch him
You feel that much cleaner.

33   The dark queen's fingernail
A curving frosted smile
The face in the pail
An enchanted isle
pale silver bone
escaped balloon
or a coin thrown
one dull afternoon
into the sky and stuck
there by some piece of luck.

34 Red river through us,
    Tributaries faintly
    Marking out their courses,
    Springing to the surface
    At the tiniest pinprick
    In terrifying beads
    That briefly glow then harden
    Crinkled as wee cowpats.

35   Look at the white cloth running on the wind.
     Look at the pebble skimmed and swallowed,
     The thousand curls and flecks that ride and fall,
     The widening circles in the heart of the valley.

     No one so clear as I am,
     I who can show you your face
     Or swallow you whole
     Or sit quietly in the smallest container
     Or run through a forest, laughing.

36 Behold the dual monarchy
    Ruling over cutlery.
    One's a scald
    The other's cold,
    But how the tears come pouring down
    When you twist that fancy crown.

37 It has a head, it has a foot
Four other feet beside,
And then two extra human feet
Covered up inside,
And underneath that snow-white sheet
The small heart's reassuring beat.

38 Little boat, where is your mast?
    You mean the leg? He's fast asleep
    Where the waves of night time sweep
    Across him. But I'm holding fast,
    Yes, I'm anchored just off-shore
    Safely on the bedroom floor.

39 Think of all those witches
Buried vertically
Only their hats showing.

Think of all those loudhailers
Whispering to tarmac
Making the whole road sing.

Think of all that red and white.
What a sight.
Mile after mile. Night after night.

40 Two armchairs, a settee,
    Rolling down the road,
    Behind a metal belly
    Within which sparks explode

    The furniture rolls on
    The sparks explode in fumes,
    Ten million mums and dads speed on
    In small upholstered rooms.

41 A wrinkled paper bowl.
    No fish swim in it,
    No water fills it up,
    But a hot sweltering
    Unbearable lightness
    Which comes on suddenly
    As if some wonderful idea
    Had struck fire in your bright head.

42 You fill my head with empty things
    So when I get to speak
    All I say is rubbish
    And that but once a week.

43 I know a man – he lives in the wall,
    He does his work by running about,
    He runs up the ceiling – and there's light!
    He runs into a box – and there is music!
    He leaps across the street and our phone rings.
    He runs about so much he gets quite hot.
    Don't touch him or he'll kick you.

44 Hundreds of stiff white legs
   On one enormous neck
   And all those legs let loose
   Inside your open mouth.

45 I saw a giraffe on the pavement
   His eye was bright though he'd been turned
      to stone
   No feet, no belly, no tail, just one long neck
   A dog sniffed at him but left him alone.

46 Grind grind
Crunch crunch
Get stuck in
It's time for lunch.

47 A long flat mouth for singing –
All those white teeth!
But the dentist never comes
To take out the black ones.

48 One hot belly
    One big ear
    One round lip
    With two more near.

49 She took a black pencil,
    Drew the eyes,
    Shaded the cheekbones
    Down to size,
    Made sure each feature
    Was properly defined,
    Then took a piece of tissue paper
    Dabbed her mouth

    And left this soft red rose behind.

Solutions

1 Doorbell

2 Traffic Lights

3 Goldfish

4 Fire

5 Lightning

6 Russian Doll

7 Wheel

8 Compasses

9 Owl

10 Glasses

11 Bicycle

12 Watch

13 Rocking Horse

14 Weathercock

15 Clothes Peg

16 Rubber Band

17 Telephone Calls

18 Robin

19 Apple Tree

20 Flag

21 Wind

22 Wheat

23 Rain

24 Sun in the Sky

25 Fingernail

26 Fingers

27 Shoe

28 Print

29 Photograph

30 Ball Point Pen

31 Scissors

32 Soap

33 Moon

34 Blood